Key Stage 2

Grammar

Carol Matchett

Introduction

Grammar is all about using words effectively. It is not just about rules – it's about putting words together and getting your message across so that everyone understands you. It's about making choices and being in control of your writing.

This book will help you understand different aspects of grammar. As your understanding improves so will your writing. The book begins by describing the different types of words and why they are important. It then goes on to explain how these words can be put together in sentences and texts.

Finding your way around this book

Before you start using this book, write your name in the name box on the first page.

Then decide how to begin. If you want a complete course on grammar, you should work right through the book from beginning to end. Another way to use the book is to dip into it when you want to find out about a particular topic, such as pronouns. The Contents page will help you to find the pages you need.

Whichever way you choose, don't try to do too much at once – it's better to work through the book in short bursts.

When you have found the topic you want to study, look out for these icons, which mark different parts of the text.

Activities

This icon shows you the activities that you should complete. You write your answers in the spaces provided. After you have worked through all the activities on the page, turn to pages 57 to 72 to check your answers. When you are sure that you understand the topic, put a tick in the box beside it on the Contents page.

On pages 45 and 56 you will find suggestions for some projects (**Now you try**), which will give you even more opportunities to improve your grammar.

Explanation

This text explains the topic and gives examples. Make sure you read it before you start the activities.

Did you know?

This text gives you useful background information about the subject.

Contents

Nouns 1

Nouns are words that name things. **Common nouns** are the words you use all the time to talk about things (objects, places, people) around you. These nouns often follow 'the', 'a' or 'an'.

Example the **table**   the **park**   a **dog**   a **girl**   an **egg**

Proper nouns are the names we give to a **particular** person, animal, place or time.

Example Rachel   Jonas   Tiddles   Manchester   April

Activities

1   Write a **common noun** in each box to complete these sentences. Your sentences can be sensible or funny. The first one has been done for you.

a   The | elephant | sat on the | wall |

b   A | | jumped over the | | .

c   My | | threw the | | into the | | .

d   The | | was waiting for a | | .

e   Asleep on the | | there was a great big | | .

2   Think of a **proper noun** (a special name) for each of these common nouns. Remember to use a **capital letter** at the start of the name.

a   ___Cuddles___ the cat   **e**   _____ the dog

b   _____ the goldfish   **f**   _____ the snake

c   _____ the hamster   **g**   _____ the lizard

d   _____ the teacher   **h**   _____ the bakers

The words **the** and **a** (or **an**) are called **articles**. Use **a** before a word that begins with a **consonant** and **an** if the word begins with a **vowel**.

Example **a b**ird   **an e**agle

Grammar

Nouns 2

Explanation

When you are writing, you need to be **clear** and **precise** in your choice of **nouns**.

Example a book → a **diary**   a **library book**   an **atlas**   a **school dictionary**

These are simple **noun phases**, made up a of a **noun** and a **determiner** – the word before the noun. In these examples the determiner is just the article **a(n)**. You can change this to a more precise determiner (such as **the**, **that**, **this**, **my**) to help **specify** which book.

Example   → **my** diary   **that** library book   **Tilly's** atlas   **this** school dictionary

Precise nouns and noun phrases like these give your reader a **clearer picture**.

Example Some **men** ran out of **a building**. → **Six firefighters** ran out of **that tower block**.

(Learn more about **phrases** on page 32.)

Activities

1 Replace these **common nouns** with **noun phrases** that give a **clearer picture**. Add some **precise nouns** to follow the **determiners**. The first line has been done for you.

Cake	Dog	Building
one chocolate éclair	our Yorkshire terrier	the Lo-Cost supermarket
this	a	that
my	an	two
an	that	the
six	her	this

2 Replace the **determiners** and **nouns** in these sentences with more **precise** choices. The first one has been done for you.

a ~~An animal~~ stole ~~the fruit~~. That baby gorilla stole my banana.

b ~~A child~~ ran into ~~a shop~~. _____

c ~~A lady~~ stood in the middle of ~~a room~~. _____

d ~~A man~~ put on ~~some clothes~~. _____

e ~~Some people~~ ran out of ~~a building~~. _____

Adjectives 1

Adjectives are words that tell you **more about a noun**. They help to **describe** or add detail. Adjectives can go before or after a noun.

Example The walker was **exhausted** as he climbed the **steep** hill.

tells us more about the walker   tells us more about the hill

Activities

1 Read this description. Underline the **adjectives** that help to describe the scene. In the box, **draw the walls** exactly as described.

The winding path led her as far as the crumbling

walls of an abandoned building. The remaining

walls were jagged and overgrown with ivy.

The floor was littered with fallen rubble.

2 Write a different adjective in each space to tell us more about the **nouns** in these sentences.

a The _____ alligators snapped at the _____ monkeys.

b The _____ cat sat on a _____ hedgehog.

c The lion was _____ but the mouse was _____ .

d A _____ wolf waited in the _____ wood.

e The _____ boy looked up at the _____ moon.

f The _____ alien thought the planet looked _____ .

g The man was _____ at the thought of crossing the _____ river.

h Rosie was _____ after the _____ game.

Did you know?

In some languages, nouns are either **masculine** or **feminine**. In these languages, adjectives are often spelt with different word endings when they are used with different types of noun.

Adjectives 2

Explanation

Adjectives are added to **noun phrases** to **describe** and **add important detail** to your writing. Choose adjectives carefully. An adjective should add **more information** about the noun, give a clearer picture or add to the overall effect of your writing.

Activities

1 Adjectives can give extra information about the size, colour and qualities of nouns. Write some more **phrases with adjectives** and **nouns** in these boxes to describe the features of animals.

Size	Colour	Qualities
enormous ears	a golden beak	a shy creature

2 Write an adjective in each box to make this description more effective.

The sky was [   ] and [   ]. It was [   ] and a

few [   ] flakes of snow were beginning to fall. Suddenly out of the gloom

a [   ] figure appeared hurrying down the road. The figure was [   ]

and [   ]. It was wearing a [   ], [   ] cloak.

3 Expand these **noun phrases** using adjectives **before and after** the noun.

a the forest   The _____ forest was _____ and _____ .

b the house   The _____ house was _____ and _____ .

c the castle walls   The _____ castle walls were _____ and _____ .

Comparatives and superlatives

Comparative adjectives are used to compare two things.

Example Mrs Jones is **old**.   ←—— adjective

                   Mrs Jones is **older** than Mr Sugden. ←—— comparative adjective

Superlative adjectives are used to show that one thing is beyond all others.

Example Mrs Jones is the **oldest** person on our street.

Activities

1 Complete this list of **comparative** and **superlative adjectives**.

   a clever → _____cleverer_____ → _____cleverest_____

   b strong → _____ → _____

   c fast   → _____ → _____

   d good   → _____better_____ → _____

2 Complete these boastful sentences by adding a **comparative** adjective and a suitable ending.

   a My dad is _____cleverer_____ than _____the winner of Mastermind._____

   b Our dog is _____ than _____ .

   c My sister is _____ than _____ .

   d Our car is _____ than _____ .

3 Choose the best **superlative** from the box to complete these adverts.

   a Wheaty Flakes – the _____ cereal yet.

   b Don't miss the _____ film of the year.

   c Test-drive the _____ car on the track.

   d This is the _____ ice cream ever tasted.

fastest
creamiest
crunchiest
funniest

With longer words, **comparatives** are made using the words **more/less**, and **superlatives** using **most/least**.

Example **more** beautiful   **less** intelligent   **most** anxious   **least** surprising

Singular and plural

Nouns can be singular or plural. **Singular** means there is **one** of something. **Plural** means there is **more than one**. Often plurals are made by **adding –s** or **–es** to the end of the noun. But some nouns have a different word ending for the plural.

Example   one dog → lots of dog**s**

one child → lots of child**ren**

Activities

Did you know?

Words like 'herd' and 'flock' are called **collective nouns**. They refer to a **singular** group that has **many** (**plural**) members.

Example
a **pack** of wolves
a **swarm** of bees
a **pride** of lions
a **pod** of dolphins
a **troop** of monkeys

1   Underline the nouns in this shopping list that are **plurals**.

I need to buy a large pizza, loaves of bread, bottles of

pop, a carton of milk, lime jellies, a pack of streamers,

cookies, party hats and a cake.

2   Write the correct **singular** or **plural** form of the **nouns**. Use a dictionary to help if you are not sure.

a   a tooth   →   many _____

b   this woman   →   those _____

c   one _____   →   two gentlemen

d   one foot _____   →   a pair of _____

e   a lone _____   →   a herd of deer

f   a single mouse   →   several _____

g   a goose   →   some _____

h   one _____   →   various people

3   Complete these sentences using suitable singular and plural nouns.

a   The farmer has a _____ of _____ and a number of _____.

b   At the market I bought a few _____ and a _____.

c   Waiting at the traffic lights, I saw several _____ but only one _____.

d   On the beach, I found countless _____ but just one _____.

Verbs 1

Verbs are important words in sentences. Verbs often tell us about actions – what someone or something is **doing**. This 'doer' of the action is called the **subject** (see page 33).

Example The cat **sits**.　　The frog **jumps**.　　A door **opens**.　　Jesse **stops**.

Some verbs tell us what someone is or has.

Example I **have** black hair.　　I **am** 10 years old.　　He **is** tired.

Activities

1 Underline the **verbs** in each of these sentences.

  a The jet engines roar as the aeroplane soars into the sky.

  b From behind a tree, the cat pounced suddenly.

  c Carly listened for a moment before she stepped forward and spoke.

  d Tigers often sleep by day and hunt at night.

2 Choose verbs from the box to complete these sentences so that they make sense.

  a Mr Samuels _____ a frightening temper.

  b Zebras _____ stripes.

  c Paris _____ the capital city of France.

  d Sophie and Isabelle _____ twins.

  e I _____ very happy today.

is
are
has
have
am

All **sentences** must have a **verb** to make sense. Even the shortest sentence needs a verb (and a subject).

Example Jon **screamed**.　　The car **crashed**.

3 Use the **nouns** and **verbs** in the boxes to make four **short sentences**.

  a The _____ .

  b A _____ .

  c The _____ .

  d _____ .

Nouns	Verbs
king	fell
rain	laughed
building	groaned
Marcie	shook

Verbs 2

Choose verbs carefully to make your writing effective. **Powerful** verbs can help suggest mood or feelings.

Example The old man **danced** around the room.   … **stomped** around the room.
                  … **tip-toed** around the room.   … **staggered** around the room.

Verbs like these hint at the old man's mood or motives.

Activities

1 Write a **verb** in each space to say what the character did. Choose a more powerful verb than the crossed-out ones below, to suggest something about the character.

a The princess ~~looked~~ _____ at the fisherman.

b The giant ~~walked~~ _____ across the hillside.

c The monster ~~ate~~ _____ his food.

d The girl ~~went~~ _____ through the trees.

e 'It's not fair,' ~~said~~ _____ Robbie.

f The man ~~got~~ _____ into the car.

2 Write a suitable verb in each space to complete this passage. Choose verbs carefully to suggest more about the characters.

Prince Fortune _____ into the hall. He _____

across the room to where the queen and princess were _____ together.

Verbs can change **tense**. Verbs have **present** and **past tenses**.

Past means something has already happened. **Present** means it is happening now.

(Learn more about verb tenses on page 24).

---

3 These sentences are in the **past tense**. Change the verbs into the **present tense**.

a I ~~heard~~ _____ a noise.   **c** I ~~raced~~ _____ outside.

b It ~~was~~ _____ late.   **d** He ~~fell~~ _____ over.

Adverbs 1

Adverbs are words that give **extra information** about **verbs** or events described in a sentence. Many adverbs give us information about **how** things happen (sadly, quickly, carefully), but some adverbs tell us **where** (here, there, outside), **when** (today, tomorrow, soon) or **how often** (always, sometimes, never).

Example The man was talking. → **Outside**, the man was talking **cheerfully**.

                              ↑   ↑

          tells us where   tells us how

Lots of adverbs that tell us **how** are formed by **adding –ly** to the end of **adjectives**.

Activities

1 Add **–ly** to the end of these **adjectives** to make a collection of **adverbs**.

a slow	_ly_	**e** sweet	_____	**i** quiet	_____
b loud	_____	**f** careful	_____	**j** cheerful	_____
c anxious	_____	**g** peaceful	_____	**k** polite	_____
d bright	_____	**h** sad	_____	**l** excited	_____

2 Write a different adverb in each space to give more information about **how** the actions are performed.

a The baby slept _____ as we _____ left the room.

b The crowd waited _____ as the music played _____.

c She _____ opened the letter, _____ unfolding each page.

d The audience listened _____ as the choir sang _____.

e He walked home _____ and _____ waited for news.

f The sun shone _____ as they _____ packed their bags.

Sometimes **adverbs** are used with **adjectives** to add **shades of meaning** to the adjective.

Example **quite** clever   **fairly** dangerous   **rather** funny   **somewhat** dull   **really** exciting
         very good   **extremely** easy   **incredibly** brave

Adverbs 2

Activities

1 Rewrite these sentences to include an **adverb** from the list. Choose a suitable adverb and **decide where** you think it should be added.

a The man spoke to his neighbours. **How often?** sometimes occasionally often never rarely

_____

b They realised their mistake. **When?**   soon later now afterwards shortly

_____

c He walked along the plank. **How?**   carefully steadily carelessly hastily

_____

d He hid the letters. **Where?**   upstairs nearby here outside everywhere

_____

2 Adverbs at the **start of a sentence** can **comment** on the event described. Choose the adverb from the brackets that best completes each sentence.

a _____ , everyone was safe.   **clearly strangely fortunately**

b _____ , this was a serious mistake.   **happily obviously surprisingly**

c _____ , the pool will close next month.   **sadly luckily apparently**

d _____ , the painting was destroyed.   **unfortunately oddly surely**

Prepositions 1

Explanation

Prepositions are little words that add **extra detail** to sentences. Words like **in**, **on**, **at**, **by**, **over**, **under** are all examples of prepositions. They are usually followed by a **noun** or **noun phrase**. A preposition and a noun (or a noun phrase) together make a **prepositional phrase**.

Example **by** the post office   **at** the bus stop   **before** noon   **since** Monday

A lot of prepositions help tell us **where** (on, in, under, over) but some prepositions tell us **when** (before, after, during, on).

Example I waited **at** the bus stop **by** the post office. ◄── **where** it happened
The shop was broken into **during** the night. ◄── **when** it happened

Activities

1 Add a **prepositional phrase** to the end of these sentences to show **where** the events happened. Use **prepositions** from the box. The first one has been done.

a The boy climbed _over the fence._	under
	over
b The girl jumped _____ .	into
	by
c The man was standing _____ .	in
	on
d The car drove _____ .	in
	through
e The ghost appeared _____ .	beside
f Marcus fell _____ .	behind

Prepositional phrases that tell us **when** something happened can be **fronted**, or **moved** to the **start** of a sentence. (Learn more about this on page 41.)

Example The game was over **by half time**.   **By half time** the game was over.

2 Add a **prepositional phrase** that tells us **when** each of these events happened. Choose a phrase from the box, or **use one of your own**.

a Jess went for a run _____ .	before breakfast
b It began to rain _____ .	after tea
c All was quiet _____ .	during the night
d They couldn't go out _____ .	on Saturday
e We went to the cinema _____ .	at midnight

Prepositions 2

Explanation

You can use **prepositional phrases** to add more **detail** about a **noun**.

Example the man **with the beard**   the man **by the gate**

which man

Activities

1 Add a **prepositional phrase** after the **noun** in each sentence. Add a second prepositional phrase at the **end** of the sentence to say **where** or **when** the event happened.

a   The **cat** _____ was sitting _____ .

b   The **path** _____ stopped _____ .

c   The **boy** _____ travelled _____ .

d   The **man** _____ was arrested _____ .

e   The **book** _____ vanished _____ .

2 Prepositional phrases are useful in all sorts of writing. Make each of these recipe instructions more **precise** by adding one of the prepositional phrases from the box.

after 20 minutes	**for** an hour	**in** a large bowl
on a baking tray	**over** a low heat	**with** a rolling pin

a   Mix the flour and sugar together _____ .

b   Heat the butter and milk _____ .

c   Roll out the mixture _____ .

d   Place the biscuits _____ .

e   Take the biscuits out of the oven _____ .

f   Leave them to cool _____ .

Pronouns 1

Explanation

Pronouns are used **in place of nouns** or noun phrases. Words like **I, she, him, it** are all examples of pronouns. Pronouns are useful because they save you having to repeat the same words over and again – which can sound awkward and long-winded.

Example Jack tried to carry **Jack's** bag but **Jack's** bag was too heavy for **Jack**.

Jack tried to carry **his** bag but **it** was too heavy for **him**.

possessive pronoun (belonging to Jack)   **personal** pronouns

Activities

1 Here are some useful **personal** and **possessive pronouns**.

I	he	she	we	they	it
me	him	her	us	them	its
mine	his	hers	ours	theirs	

Rewrite these sentences using pronouns in place of the crossed-out words.

a ~~Kavita and I~~ went to the shop but ~~the shop~~ was closed.

_____

b ~~Elliot~~ had lost **Elliot's** coat and could not find ~~the coat~~ anywhere.

_____

c The twins were playing in the garden but ~~the twins'~~ sister did not see ~~the twins~~.

_____

d Nina knew that the book was **Nina's** but ~~Nina~~ did not want ~~the book~~.

_____

e The man was following ~~Seth and me~~ and ~~Seth and I~~ were worried.

_____

f Jordan thought ~~Jordan~~ had won the race, but ~~Jordan~~ should have looked behind ~~Jordan~~.

_____

Pronouns 2

Explanation

Pronouns are very useful, but sometimes get **overused**. This can lead to **confusing** writing.

Example Carrie went to see Alice. **She** was angry. ← **who** was angry?

Always make sure it is clear who or what each pronoun refers to.

Activities

1 In this well-known story, the author has used so many **pronouns** that it is not clear which character is being referred to. Rewrite the story **changing some** (but not all) of the pronouns back to the names of the characters.

The tortoise and the hare waited for the gun to start the race. Bang! Immediately he flew out of the blocks. His long legs ate up the ground and soon he was completely out of sight. Meanwhile, he had only just crossed the starting line. His little legs did not move very fast. Looking back from the top of the hill, he saw him and laughed.

_____

_____

_____

_____

_____

_____

Pronouns can be used to make **links between sentences**.

Example Sheena suggested we should go back. **This** seemed like a good idea.

↑

Sheena's suggestion

---

2 What do the pronouns in these sentences refer back to?

a The old man opened the box. **It** was empty.   **It =** <u>the box</u>

b Will went first. I said **that** was not fair.   **that =** _____

c Hannah won the race. **This** was a surprise.   **This =** _____

d Later we went to a film. **It** was great.   **It =** _____

Conjunctions

Explanation

Conjunctions are words that **link** or connect together ideas **within a sentence**. Words like **when, while, so, because, although** are all examples of conjunctions. They help us to join different parts of a sentence together. (These parts are called **clauses** – see page 32).

Example The tortoise plodded on **until** he found the hare asleep under the tree.

      ↑   ↑   ↑

      clause 1   **conjunction**   clause 2

Activities

1   Choose a **conjunction** from the box to complete these sentences.

unless	as	although	because	when	since

a   The old man continued on his way _____ it was getting dark.

b   Do not enter the room _____ a green light is showing.

c   Everyone rushed towards the river _____ the fire spread out of control.

d   He fell asleep in his chair _____ he was so tired.

e   _____ he saw the food, he gobbled it up immediately.

f   _____ it is already six o'clock, let's tidy away.

2   Different conjunctions link ideas in different ways. Write an ending for each sentence to fit the conjunction given.

a   The monster roared loudly **when** _____ .

b   The monster roared loudly **because** _____ .

c   The monster roared loudly **although** _____ .

d   The monster roared loudly **until** _____ .

e   The monster roared loudly **so** _____ .

f   The monster roared loudly **while** _____ .

Editing: word choice

Explanation

Think about your **choice of words** when you are **editing** your work. Do your **adjectives** and **noun phrases** add important detail? Does your choice of **verbs** and **adverbs** add to the overall effect? If not, then change, add or delete words to **make your meaning clear** or to achieve the **effect** you want.

Did you know?

The word '**text**' (meaning 'a piece of writing') comes from the Latin word 'texere', which means 'to weave'. Think of writing as choosing rich and colourful words and then weaving them together to produce the finished text.

Activities

1 Rewrite this description and improve it by making the setting sound more impressive. Use **expanded noun phrases** to achieve the effect. Change or add **nouns**, **adjectives** and **prepositional phrases**.

Two doors opened to reveal the ballroom. The room was full of people, all dancing. The walls were all white and the ceiling was patterned. There were red curtains hanging at the windows.

_____

_____

_____

_____

_____

_____

2 Write a better **verb** in each box to replace the crossed-out verbs in this passage. Choose words carefully for **effect.**

Grey-black clouds ~~went~~ [   ] across the sky. The branches on the trees ~~moved~~

[   ] in the wind and the leaves ~~fell~~ [   ] all around.

Raindrops ~~fell~~ [   ] on the windowpane and ~~dropped~~ [   ] in puddles

on the pavement. People ~~went~~ [   ] down the road towards their homes. They

~~went~~ [   ] with their umbrellas in the wind and rain.

Understanding word classes 1

You have now looked at the different types, or **classes**, of words. These pages will help you to check your understanding of the different classes and how to use them.

Here are some of the **main classes of words** you have looked at.

A noun **B adjective** **C verb** **D adverb** **E preposition** **F conjunction**

Activities

1 Put a letter in each box to show the **word classes** in this sentence.

The thirsty elephant lumbered down to the watering hole.

2 What **class of word** is missing from each of these sentences? Write the class of word in the box.

a Slowly, the old [ ] shuffled along the [ ] street.

b The fearful child [ ] anxiously to its mother.

c The grand old gentleman waited patiently [ ] the hallway.

d The lion [ ] stalked its prey.

e The waves became stronger [ ] the wind whipped the surface of the sea.

3 Write examples of words from the different **classes** to make sentences.

	Adjective	Noun	Verb	Prepositional phrase
The	chattering	monkey	swings	through the trees.
An				
The				
A				
A				

Understanding word classes 2

1 Put a letter in each box to show the **word classes** in this sentence.

A conjunction   **B preposition**   **C pronoun**   **D determiner**

Tom hid **in** **the** shed **because** **he** was scared.

2 Find a **preposition** that can complete all three sentences. Write it in the spaces.

Meet me _____ the bridge. Come _____ bike. Arrive _____ noon at the latest.

3 Add the correct **articles** before each **noun** in this sentence.

_____ doctor said that eating _____ apple _____ day is _____ good idea.

4 Some **pronouns** are missing from these sentences. Write them in the spaces.

a We had lost _____ way. We shouted but no-one heard _____ .

b They all went back to _____ rooms and left _____ by myself.

5 Choose the most suitable **conjunction** to complete each sentence.

| as | until | before | after | but |

a Always wash your hands _____ you eat food.

b Stir the porridge _____ it is smooth.

c He became a chef _____ he left school.

d The match will be cancelled _____ it is snowing.

e I would like a dog _____ I am not allowed one.

6 Sometimes we use too many **adjectives**. Cross out the unnecessary adjectives in this sentence.

Three butterflies danced together in the bright, dazzling, glorious early morning sunshine.

Cohesion: linking ideas 1

Explanation

Some words and phrases help to **link ideas** and give your writing **cohesion**.

Conjunctions link together ideas **within a sentence** (see page 18). **Adverbials** can help link together ideas in **separate sentences** or across paragraphs. These linking adverbials can be either **adverbs** or **prepositional phrases**. They show how ideas fit together or follow on.

Example Cinderella was delighted with the dress. **However**, it did not help her get to the ball.

sentence 1   **adverbial** (linking contrasting ideas)   sentence 2

Activities

1 Different **adverbials** link ideas together in different ways. Underline the one that **best links** the ideas in each pair of sentences.

  a   The children were hoping to go to the beach. **Also, However**, it rained all day.

  b   It was snowing heavily this morning. **As a result, Finally** lots of people were late for school.

  c   We visited the famous landmarks in Paris. **Next, For example**, we went to the Eiffel Tower.

  d   Our train was over an hour late. **Eventually, Before** we arrived at our destination.

  e   Firstly, the trainers were not really what I wanted. **Secondly, Finally** they were too expensive.

  f   It was fine all day today. **Furthermore, Meanwhile, In contrast**, it rained all yesterday.

2 Adverbials are useful when developing ideas. Write a second **sentence** that could follow each of these adverbials.

  a   Many people use their cars every day.

  For example, _____ .

  b   Many people use their cars every day.

  On the other hand, _____ .

  c   Many people use their cars every day.

  As a consequence, _____ .

  d   Many people use their cars every day.

  After all, _____ .

Cohesion: linking ideas 2

Time adverbials help to make clear the time or **sequence of events**.

Example next   later   meanwhile   suddenly   after that   now   at that moment   finally

Activities

1 Here are the main events from the story of Red Riding Hood. Add a **time adverbial** before each event to show the **time or sequence** of the events. (Don't use the word 'then'.)

Red Riding Hood was walking through the forest.

_____ a wolf jumped out and surprised her.

_____ Red Riding Hood went on her way again.

_____ the wolf rushed to Granny's house.

_____ Red Riding Hood arrived at Granny's house.

_____ the wolf tried to eat Red Riding Hood.

_____ a woodcutter rushed in and killed the wolf.

_____ everyone was safe.

Some **adverbials** are used to show **cause and effect**. They show how one event causes or leads to another.

Example The sun came out. **As a result**, the washing dried quickly.

2 Complete the second sentence to show what might happen **as a result of** the event described in the first sentence. The first one has been done for you.

a It has not rained for several weeks. **Consequently,** _the ground is very dry._

b The wind fills the sails of the yacht. **As a result,** _____.

c The handles on the bag were not very strong. **Therefore** _____.

d The lions had not eaten for some time. **Because of this** _____.

Verb tenses 1

Explanation

The word **tense** refers to the time **when** something happens. **Verbs** have different tense **forms**. They can be in the **past** or **present** tense.

Example I **go** and **play** outside. ⟵ present tense

Yesterday, I **went** and **played** outside. ⟵ past tense

Many **regular** past tense forms **end –ed**, but some verbs are **irregular**, such as **go → went**.

Activities

1 These sentences are written in the **present tense**. Rewrite each sentence, changing the **verb** to the **past tense**.

a It **is** hot today. → It was hot last week.

b I **hear** a strange sound. → _____ .

c I **jump** high. → _____ .

d I **take** my time. → _____ .

e Ed **runs** for the bus. → _____ .

2 Add a verb to complete each sentence, keeping to the **same tense**.

a Birds live in trees where they _____ nests.

b Cara realised she was late when she _____ the bus.

c I always help to wash up and _____ the kitchen.

d We ate our breakfast before we _____ our bags.

e George enters and _____ in the armchair.

f He was tired as he _____ into bed.

Did you know?

Languages such as French, Spanish or Italian have a **future tense** with different verb forms or endings. English does not have a future tense like this. To talk about things that are yet to happen, in English we use present tense **main verbs** with other verbs such as **will**, **shall**, **is/are going**.

Example Next week **we are going** to begin our journey. We **will leave** early.

Verb tenses 2

Activities

1 Read this commentary on a sporting event. Rewrite it using the **–ing form** of the **verbs**, as if the race is in progress. The first line has been started for you.

Marshall (leads) at the bell but Jackson (closes) on him again. The fans (go) mad.
Marshall (sprints) down the back straight but Jackson and the others (chase) hard.

<u> Marshall is leading at the bell</u>

_____

_____

_____

2 On a separate piece of paper rewrite your commentary in the **past tense** still using the **–ing form** of verbs. Start: Marshall was leading …

3 Use the perfect **has/have form** of verbs to complete these sentences.

a I _____ the film six times. It's great!

b Mum says she _____ a letter to the Prime Minister.

c I think Dad _____ shopping.

d I _____ too much chocolate. Now I feel sick.

e Be careful – someone _____ a glass.

f You can't swim today if you _____ your trunks.

First, second and third person 1

Explanation

Writing can be in the **first person** when the writer speaks about **him/herself**
second person when the writer speaks **to the reader**
third person when the writer speaks about **someone** (or something) **else**.

Notice how the **verbs** and **pronouns** change in these examples.

Example **I am** late. ⟵ **first person** (the writer speaking about him/herself)
You are late. ⟵ **second person** (the writer speaking to the reader)
He is late. ⟵ **third person** (the writer speaking about someone else)

Activities

1 Add the **pronouns** needed to complete these sentences. Make sure you keep to **first**, **second** or **third person**.

a My name is Megan and _____ live in Cardiff with _____ family.

b The children tried to carry _____ bags but _____ were too heavy for _____.

c Have you ever had problems with _____ computer?

d Mrs Quinn called Arthur and me into _____ office. _____ wondered what _____ had done.

e He could not do it by _____. _____ needed someone to help _____.

2 Below you can read what Lucy has written about herself. Rewrite the information about Lucy using the **third person**.

I am 11 years old and I go to Midfield School in Stonington. When I grow up I would really like to be a singer and have lots of hits.

Lucy is 11 years old and _____

_____

_____

_____

_____

_____

_____

_____

First, second and third person 2

Explanation

The **first person** is used for personal writing such as diaries, personal letters and autobiographies. The **second person** is often used in instructions or to address the reader. The **third person** is usually used in reports and information writing.

Accounts and stories can be written in the first or third person. The first person gives a much more **personal** view of events.

Activities

1 Here is an extract from a story that is written in the **third person**.

The fisherman had been working all day, but still he had not caught one fish. He pulled up the last of his nets – it was empty, like all the others. The fisherman thought how unlucky he was. What would he tell his children? Just then something in the water caught his eye. The fisherman looked over the side of the boat to get a better look …

Rewrite the story in the **first person** – as if the fisherman were telling the story.

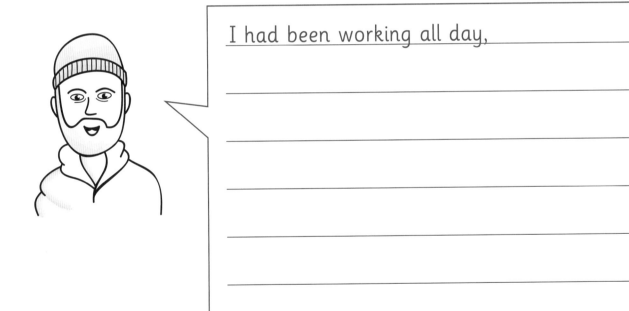

I had been working all day,

When you are writing in the **first person**, be careful with the **pronouns I** and **me**. Use **I** before a verb and **me** after a verb.

Example I helped.   Zoë and I helped.   ◄— **subject** (I do the action)
     She helped **me**.   She helped Zoë and **me**.   ◄— **object** (the action is done to **me**)

Subject and verb agreement

Verbs can change their form depending on the **person** or **subject** (see page 33) you are writing about. It is important to choose the **verb form** that matches or **agrees** with the **subject** of the sentence.

Example **I have** a brother.   **He has** a brother.   **They have** a brother.
            I am 10 years old.   **She is** 10 years old.   **They are** 10 years old.
            I play the guitar.   **He plays** the guitar.   **They play** the guitar.

Say the sentence in your head before writing it down. Check that it sounds right.

Activities

1   Check the **verbs** in these sentences. Put a **tick** in the box if the **subject** and **verb agree**. Put a **cross** if the wrong form of the verb has been chosen.

a   **He play** for the school team.   ☐   d   **They was** surprised by the result.   ☐

b   **We were** really pleased.   ☐   e   Yes, **I done** it.   ☐

c   **I hates** cheese and onion crisps.   ☐   f   **You have** five more minutes.   ☐

2   You should have found four sentences where the wrong **verb form** has been chosen. Rewrite these four sentences using the **correct** verb.

_____

_____

_____

_____

3   Complete these sentences by choosing the **correct form** of the verb from the box.

a   You _____ happy.

b   She _____ lots of friends.

c   I _____ pleased.

d   They _____ a beautiful house.

e   He _____ tired.

are
is
am
has
have

Standard English

Explanation

Standard English is used in most **writing**. Although you might use other forms when you speak, it is important to use Standard English in your writing. Here are some common errors to avoid.

Example	them books	✗	**those** books	✓	(Standard English)
	the race what I won	✗	the race **that** I won	✓	(Standard English)
	It was real good	✗	it was **really** good	✓	(Standard English)
	Polly and me helped.	✗	Polly and **I** helped.	✓	(Standard English)

(See page 27 for more about when to use **I** and **me**.)

Activities

1 Check these sentences. Underline the word that needs changing and write it correctly.

a Zac and me ran all the way home. _____

b Look at them horses in the field. _____

c I done my homework last night. _____

d I'll have one of them cakes. _____

e This is the book what I read. _____

f Here is a real funny joke. _____

It is important not to use **two negative words** in a sentence.

Example I **never** said **nothing**. (meaning that you *did* say something)

---

2 Write the correct version of these sentences. The first one has been done for you.

a I never said ~~nothing~~. I never said anything. _____

b Nobody did ~~nothing~~ to help. _____

c I never saw ~~nobody~~. _____

d I don't like ~~nothing~~ here. _____

Editing: checking consistency

When you are writing there are a lot of things to remember. It is easy to use too many **pronouns** or to forget which **tense** or **person** you are writing in. This is why it is important to **read through your writing** and **check** that everything **makes sense**, and is **clear, complete** and **consistent**.

Activities

1 Read through this piece of writing. **Check** that the writing is **complete** and **makes sense** – for example, that it keeps to the same **tense**. **Make changes** where they are needed.

On Saturday, we went watch the school football team play in the Player's Cup.

It a very exciting game. The final score was 2–2, was probably a fair result

because both teams play well. Our team scores first thanks to awesome free

kick from Jake Edwards. But then they equalise just before the whistle goes

for half-time.

2 Read these sentences, checking the use of **pronouns**. Underline anything that is wrong, inconsistent or unclear. Make any changes that are needed.

a Evie and Emily had left her coats on the bus.

b Jack ran to the top of the beanstalk and he ran after him.

c After we finished, Jordan and me were exhausted.

d Becky was worried about Ethan and me. She tried to call them.

e David couldn't open the door without the wizard's key. It was locked and he knew it was still in his workshop.

Editing: grammatical errors

Explanation

It is also important to check that everything is **grammatically correct** in your writing. Remember to check that **subjects and verbs agree** (see page 28) and that you have used **Standard English** forms (see page 29).

Activities

1 Check these sentences to see if they are **grammatically correct**. Underline any words that need to be changed and write the corrections.

a The old man said he weren't hungry. _____

b I think the computer is broked. _____

c Everyone have forgotten about us. ____ ____ ____

d Mrs Gardiner gave me them old photos. _____

e The film what we saw was real sad. _____

f I have writ the date in me diary. _____

2 Check that everything is grammatically correct in this piece of writing. Change any words that do not sound right.

                                   live

Let me tell you about my family. We ~~lives~~ in a house on the corner of

Grant Street. I has two sisters and a older brother. My sisters am twins.

My brother and me share a room. My brother says he don't like sharing

with me because he hasn't no space for his things. Sometimes the twins

and me plays together, but sometimes we argue.

Did you know?

Standard English is used all over the world, wherever English is spoken. Even if people have different accents or different ways of saying things, they still need Standard English when writing.

Phrases and clauses

Sentences are made up of **words**, **phrases** and **clauses**.

A **phrase** is a group of **words** that go together. A **noun phrase** includes words that go with a noun. A **prepositional phrase** starts with a preposition, usually followed by a noun phrase.

A **clause** is a special type of phrase – a group of words that includes a **verb**. Sentences are often made up of a clause and one or more additional phrases. The **clause** tells us the most **important information** and the **phrases** give **extra information**.

Example **In a far and distant land**, there once lived a wise man **with three sons**.

     prepositional phrase   clause   prepositional phrase

Activities

1 Write a label to show whether the **bold** part of each sentence is a **phrase** or a **clause**.

a Then **we went back** to the farmhouse.

b They ran **on the soft grass**.

c The man caught **a large fish**.

d **The man drove off** in the sports car.

e On Monday, **Vishal woke early**.

f **Polar bears** live in the Arctic.

2 Choose phrases from the box to add to the start and end of these clauses. You can use a phrase more than once.

with the class	in a car	within seconds
in the morning	in the corridor	only the other day

a _____ the teacher was furious _____ .

b _____ the robber had escaped _____ .

c _____ a boy slipped _____ .

d _____ I saw Mrs Johnson _____ .

One-clause sentences

Explanation

A **sentence** is a group of words that tells us something and **makes sense by itself**. A simple or basic sentence has **one main clause**, often with just a **subject** and a **verb**.

Example The dragon flew away.

This **one-clause sentence** can be made longer by adding adverbs, adjectives and prepositional phrases that give extra information about the event.

Example **Fearfully**, the **little** dragon flew away **from the smoking mountain**.

Activities

1 Here are some **phrases**. Make each one into a **complete sentence**.

a the angry lion   → <u>The angry lion glared through the metal bars.</u>

b pieces on the floor   → _____

c two pointed ears   → _____

d on the way to school → _____

e the excited children   → _____

> The **subject** is the 'doer' of the action. The **object** is the person or thing affected by the action.

2 Write a **one-clause sentence** that includes the verb **chased**. **Underline** the **subject** of your sentence and draw a **ring** round the **object**.

_____ .

3 Select a **verb** from the box to help make each of these phrases into a one-clause sentence. Add a phrase of your own to complete the sentence.

a The horse <u>trotted down the road</u> _____ . | fluttered

b The rock climbers _____ . | trotted

c The witch _____ . | vanished

d A butterfly _____ . | barked

e A dog _____ . | clambered

Joining main clauses

Activities

1 Rewrite each pair of sentences as a **two-clause sentence**. Use one of these **co-ordinating conjunctions** to join the sentences together.

and	but	or

a I missed the bus. I wasn't late.

_____

b The windows were open. I could hear birds singing.

_____

c He picked up all the rubbish. He put it in the bin.

_____

d It will be dry in the north. There will be rain in the south.

_____

e We could go to the zoo. We could go into town.

_____

2 Complete these sentences by adding another **main clause**.

a The car stopped **and** _____ .

The car stopped **but** _____ .

b Alex was tired **but** _____ .

Alex was tired **and** _____ .

c Simone can play football **but** _____ .

Simone can play football **or** _____ .

Grammar

Subordinate clauses 1

Activities

1   Read these sentences. Draw a **solid** line under the **main clause** and a dotted line under the **subordinate clause**.

a   The dog snarled at her, which made her nervous.

b   Although his heart was pounding, Emil stepped forward.

c   While she was reading, the doorbell rang.

d   The lights came on one at a time until the whole street was lit up.

e   When the factory closed, many people lost their jobs.

f   Stretch the fabric over the card, folding the edges under neatly.

2   Add a **main clause** to each of these subordinate clauses so the sentences make sense.

a   As it was dark, _____ .

b   When we arrived home, _____ .

c   _____ because it was cold.

d   _____ after winning the lottery.

e   _____ when he fell over.

f   Peering through the window, _____ .

g   _____ , which really annoyed me.

Subordinate clauses 2

Explanation

You can add a **subordinate** clause to a **main** clause by using a **subordinating conjunction** (like **so**, **as**, **when**, **because**). The conjunction introduces the subordinate clause and **shows how the ideas link** together.

Example The man was pleased to be home **as** he opened his front door.
He was pleased to be home **because** he was very tired.

Activities

1 Add a suitable **subordinate clause** to follow each **conjunction**.

a Dad enjoys cooking **because** _____.

b Dad enjoys cooking **whenever** _____.

c Dad enjoys cooking **whereas** _____.

d Dad enjoys cooking **until** _____.

e Dad enjoys cooking **though** _____.

f Dad enjoys cooking **as long as** _____.

Some **subordinate clauses** start with the **–ing** or **–ed** form of a **verb**.

Example **Pleased to be home**, the man opened the door.
Opening his door, he was pleased to be home.

---

2 Link these ideas into **one sentence**. Use a subordinate clause starting with the **verb** from the first sentence. The first one has been started for you.

a Ellen was standing by the door. She watched the storm approaching.

Standing by the door, _____.

b The car was travelling at speed. It just missed the approaching lorry.

_____

c The runner was encouraged by the crowd. He sprinted for the line.

_____

Relative clauses

Activities

1 Rewrite these sentences, adding the information from the brackets as a **relative clause**.

a Paula refused to move. (She was exhausted.)

Paula, who _____ , refused to move.

b Mr King was now very late. (He had left early.)

Mr King, _____ , was now very late.

c The beggar pleaded for help. (He was penniless.)

The beggar, _____ , pleaded for help.

d The house once belonged to my father. (It is now empty.)

The house, _____ , once belonged to my father.

e The vase lay on the floor. (It was broken.)

The vase, _____ , lay on the floor.

2 Choose the **relative pronoun** from the brackets to complete each sentence.

a We found the street _____ Tarik lives.   **when where which that**

b Today was the exam _____ she was dreading.   **when where whose that**

c I saw Joanna, _____ mother was waiting outside.   **which where whose that**

d That was the day _____ it all began.   **when whose where which**

e He chose the red door, _____ was a mistake.   **when where which whose**

Sentence types 1

Some sentences are **statements**, some are **questions** and some are **commands**. By making small changes you can **change the type of sentence** you are writing.

Example **You are** going to school. ◄—— statement
          Are you going to school? ◄—— question
          Go to school. ◄—— command

To make a **statement** into a **question**, you **change the word order**.
To make either of these into a **command**, you **move the verb** to the **start** of the sentence.

Activities

1 Use the words from the box to make a **statement** and then a **question**.
The first one has been done for you.

a | planning a holiday you are |

Statement: _You are planning a holiday._

Question: _____?

b | cold it is |

Statement: _____.

Question: _____?

c | bored you are |

Statement: _____.

Question: _____?

d | help me you can |

Statement _____.

Question _____?

2 Rewrite each statement as a **command**. The first one has been done for you.

a Statement: We take the dog for a walk every day.

Command: _Take the dog for a walk every day._

b Statement: We are going to visit Hammington Hall this weekend.

Command: _____

c Statement: We always eat lots of fruit and vegetables.

Command: _____

Sentence types 2

Explanation

Exclamations are very **short** sentences that express **emotion**.

Example Help!

Some exclamations don't even have a verb.

Example Oh, no!   Wow!   What a mess!

Activities

1 Read these sentences. Tick the two that are **statements**.

a This game is really simple. ☐   There should be five counters. ☐

Take out the pieces. ☐   Are you ready to play? ☐

Place them on the table. ☐   Let's go. ☐

b Copy the particular words that show three of the sentences are **commands**.

_____   _____   _____

c Which sentence could be an **exclamation**? Write it here.

_____!

2 Turn these **questions** into **commands**. The first one has been done for you.

a Could you help me?   → _Help me._____

b Can you hold this end?   → _____

c Did you want to put that down?   → _____

d Have you tried this new ice cream? → _____

e Will you come and visit soon?   → _____

3 You can make your writing sound lively and interesting by using different types of sentences.
Read this advert for Supakleena. Label the **statement**, the **question** and the **command**.

a | **Would you like a cleaner kitchen?** → _____

b | **Use new Supakleena.** → _____

c | **It cleans kitchens fast.** → _____

Placing adverbials

Explanation

Adverbials are the **words**, **phrases** and subordinate **clauses** that tell us **more about the main clause** in a sentence. Adverbials can often be **moved around** within the sentence.

Example A figure crept cautiously across the garden as the shadows lengthened.

All these adverbials are put **after** the **main clause** but they can be **fronted**, or moved to the **start** of the sentence.

Example **As the shadows lengthened**, a figure crept cautiously across the garden.
Cautiously, a figure crept across the garden as the shadows lengthened.
Across the garden, as the shadows lengthened, a figure crept cautiously.

Starting sentences with **fronted adverbials** can be very effective. Try saying different versions of a sentence and listen for the **effects** created.

Activities

1 Rewrite these sentences moving an **adverb** or **adverbial** to the **start** of the sentence. **Try out** ideas in your head to see which version you think sounds the best.

a   The princess dropped the message **hurriedly out of the window**.

_____

b   The villagers were waiting **anxiously at midnight**.

_____

c   The explorers went without food **frequently during this time**.

_____

d   Danny was in trouble **at school usually**.

_____

2 Arrange these **words** and **phrases** to make **three** different versions of the sentence.

he strode	the town	purposefully	through

_____

_____

_____

Placing subordinate clauses

Placing a **subordinate clause** at the **start** of a sentence helps vary sentence openings and can create an interesting **effect**.

Example He spun round **as the door slammed shut**.
As the door slammed shut, he spun round.

Activities

1 Rewrite these sentences moving the **subordinate clause** to the **start** of the sentence.

a Everything was quiet **until the storm began**.

_____

b The man strolled along the street **humming merrily**

_____

c The match was a draw **despite playing extra time**.

_____

d She had to train hard **to achieve perfection**.

_____

2 Write a **subordinate clause** to **start** each sentence with an interesting or dramatic **detail** about the event.

a _____ , the man returned home.

b _____ , Tim hid in the tree.

c _____ , she did not stop.

d _____ , the car sped off.

e _____ , the evil queen laughed.

3 Move the subordinate clause in **bold** to the **middle** of this sentence.

I won't know if I have won **until I receive the letter**.

I won't know _____ if I have won.

Multi-clause sentences

Activities

1 **Combine** the information from each series of three sentences into one **multi-clause sentence**.

a The sun began to rise. The grey world became lighter. The birds awoke from their sleep.

_____

_____

b Lee was feeling more confident. He climbed to the top of the ladder. He paused for a moment.

_____

_____

c The sloth is a slow-moving mammal. It lives in trees. It hangs upside down from branches.

_____

_____

d He walked quickly. He followed the mysterious figure. It crossed the marketplace.

_____

_____

e The waves wash over the cliffs. Some rocks are worn away. The rocks fall into the sea.

_____

_____

Editing: sentence construction

Explanation

Effective writing uses a variety of **different types of sentence**. **One-clause sentences** are **clear** and to the point, but too many will make your writing sound jerky. **Multi-clause sentences** can **link** ideas and make writing **flow**, but if they are too long they will sound confusing.

A **mixture** of different kinds of sentences is usually most effective.

Activities

1 This paragraph uses only **one-clause sentences**. See if you can make it more effective by using a mixture of **different types** of sentence. **Make changes** where you can improve it.

One day Anya and Leon went to the canal. They were going fishing. There seemed to be no-one else around. They chose the best place. They started to get out the rods. Suddenly there was a loud splash. Then there was a scream. Anya and Leon looked up. They saw something moving in the water. They saw a hand waving. Someone had fallen into the water.

2 This next extract is **all one** sentence. See if you can make the meaning clearer by splitting it into **separate** sentences. Make any changes that you think will improve it.

Human beings need food in order to live so every part of the body needs a steady supply of food so that it can work properly so first the food has to be broken down through a process called digestion so that it can dissolve in the blood and travel around the body.

3 Here are four sentences advertising a new computer game. Change **three** of the sentences to make a **statement**, a **question**, a **command** and an **exclamation**.

Some computer games are slow and dull. _____

Manic Heroes is a fantastic new computer game for kids. _____

You can order it today. _____

It's a really great game. _____

Understanding sentence terms

1 **Underline** the **subject** of this one-clause sentence. Draw a **ring** round the **object**.

Mr Watkins lost his umbrella.

2 Write a **one-clause sentence** about this picture.

Underline the subject. Draw a ring round the object.

_____

_____

3 **Negative sentences** use words such as **not, never, nobody, nothing.**

  a Write a negative sentence about the sentence in activity 1.

  _____

  b Write a negative sentence about the picture in activity 2.

  _____

4 Add each type of **clause** to the **start**, **middle** or **end** of the sentence in activity 1.

  a A main clause: _____

  b A relative clause: _____

  c A subordinate clause: _____

5 Sometimes **repeated** or **predictable words** in a sentence can be **missed out**. Put **brackets** round the words that could be missed out of these sentences.

  a I'd like to help Mr Watkins but I cannot help Mr Watkins.

  b Mr Watkins found his umbrella and Mr Watkins put it up.

  c I gave him my umbrella because I wanted to give him my umbrella.

Each of these writing projects lets you focus on using a particular class of words.

Keep a diary

Keep a diary and write about all the things you do. Make sure that you use the right pronouns to refer to your friends (they, he or she), you and your family (we) and yourself (I). Make sure it is clear who the pronouns refer to – or you won't know who did what!

Spend a million

Imagine you had a million pounds to spend. Write your shopping list. Use precise nouns, adjectives and expanded noun phrases to describe your desirable items. For example, instead of writing just 'shoes', you might want sparkly red shoes with silver bows … or neon trainers with go-faster stripes.

Around and about

Set up a treasure trail or assault course for your family or friends. Write detailed directions for them to follow. Use prepositional phrases to show where to go or look – for example, 'climb under the net', 'look behind the shed'.

The conjunction game

Write some conjunctions on pieces of card and put them in a box. Then play this game with a friend. Say a short sentence and draw out a conjunction. See who can come up with the most interesting, amusing or silliest ending for the sentence.

Verb collector

Become a verb collector. Collect interesting verbs in a notebook. Find your verbs in books, poems or any materials you read. Organise the verbs under headings – for example, Sports report verbs, Suspense verbs, Verbs instead of 'said'.

Fun and games

Play the verb or adverb game with your friends. This is like charades but you mime interesting verbs or adverbs rather than titles. First write some interesting verbs or 'how' – adverbs on separate pieces of paper. Then take it in turns to pick one out and mime it.

Possibility: modal verbs

Activities

1 Add **modal verbs** so these **future** events seem **possible** but **not certain**.

a We _____ win our next game.

b It _____ rain tomorrow.

c She _____ be late today.

d I _____ see you tomorrow.

e I _____ go out later.

f It _____ work.

2 Add modal verbs to make these **statements** sound **certain**.

a It _____ help.

b You _____ go to the ball.

c It _____ be true.

d We _____ do this.

e I _____ be there.

f It _____ be cold.

3 Rewrite these statements to sound **less likely**, more like **possibilities**.

a I have the answer. _____

b She will win first prize. _____

c This will solve the problem. _____

d It is his best book yet. _____

e It is too late. _____

4 Write a horoscope with **predictions** about what **might happen** in the week ahead. Use modal verbs to show **how likely** the events are.

In the week ahead you **could** meet lots of new and interesting people.

_____

_____

Possibility: adverbs

Some **adverbs** show different **levels of possibility**.

Example It will **possibly** happen.   It will **probably** happen.   **Of course** it will happen.

These adverbs help to show how **likely** or **unlikely** you think an event is.

Activities

1 Sort these **adverbs** to show different **levels of possibility**.

certainly	possibly	surely	never	perhaps
maybe	seldom	definitely	rarely	

Very likely: _____   _____   _____

Possible: _____   _____   _____

Not very likely: _____   _____   _____

2 Add an **adverb** to make these statements sound **very likely.**

a   He will _____ succeed.

b   This is _____ the best.

c   _____, it will work.

d   _____, he told the truth.

e   This plant will _____ die.

f   I will _____ be there.

g   They are _____ wrong.

h   It will _____ rain today.

3 Complete the second sentence with a suitable **possibility**.

a   The letter did not arrive today. **Maybe** _____.

b   Our star striker is injured. He **might possibly** _____.

c   I have lost my coat. **Perhaps** _____.

d   Max did not come. He **probably** _____.

e   We can't do this alone. **Maybe** _____.

f   It is still raining. **Perhaps** _____.

Conditional sentences 1

A **conditional sentence** has two clauses. The **main clause depends** on the events or situation described in the other clause.

Example If it is sunny at the weekend, we will go camping.

          ↑   ↑

    subordinate **if**-clause   main clause

Modal verbs like **will**, **would**, **could** are often used in conditional sentences.

Activities

1 Complete these **conditional sentences** by adding a **main clause** that says what you **would** do in each imaginary situation.

a If I had a magic wand, I _____.

b If I were famous, I _____.

c I _____ if I won the lottery.

d If I were invisible, I _____.

e If I had a magic carpet, _____.

f _____ if I ruled the world.

2 Complete these conditional sentences suggesting what **will most likely happen** as a result of these actions.

a If we continue to destroy the forests, _____.

b If everyone drops litter in the street, _____.

c If everyone switches off one light, _____.

d If Jack decides to climb the beanstalk, _____.

e If they cannot escape from the dragon's cave, _____.

f _____ if we all practise hard.

In **formal writing**, the **subjunctive** form 'were' is often used instead of 'was' in **if**-clauses.

Example If I **were** rich …   If I **were** famous …   If I **were** you …

Conditional sentences 2

Modal verbs like **could**, **might**, **may** are used in conditional sentences to show different **shades of meaning**.

Example If it is sunny, we **could** … **might** … **may** … go camping.
If I were rich, I **could** … **might** … **may** … buy a mansion.

Activities

1 Complete these **conditional sentences** to show a range of **possibilities**.

a If it continues to rain, we **will** _____ .

If it continues to rain we **could** _____ .

If it continues to rain we **might** _____ or we **may even**

_____ .

b If I keep practising I **will** _____ .

If I keep practising I **could** _____ .

If I keep practising I **might** _____ and I **may even**

_____ .

2 Some conditional sentences look back on events and suggest how things **could have been different**. Complete the **if-clause** in these sentences. The first one has been done for you.

a If ___you had picked up the banana skin___ , **I would not have** slipped over.

b If _____ , we **could have** won the game.

c If _____ , I **might have** arrived on time.

d If _____ , you **might have** known the answer.

e If _____ , it **would have** hit the lorry.

f If _____ , I **could have** seen the sunrise.

Active and passive sentences 1

Explanation

Active and passive versions of a sentence say the same thing but the **focus is different**.

Example The pirates hid the treasure.   ⟵ **active**   (subject: the **pirates**)
          The treasure was hidden by the pirates. ⟵ **passive** (subject: the **treasure**)

The **active sentence** is about the pirates, **who do the action**.
The **passive sentence** is about **what happens to** the treasure, not the action of the pirates.

To change from **active to passive**, you move the **new subject** (the treasure) to **before the verb**, and **change the verb form** from active (hid) to passive (was hidden).

Activities

1   Rewrite these **active** sentences in the **passive voice**. The first one has been done for you.

Example The children put on a play. → A play **was put on** by the children.

a   Everybody enjoyed the show.

→ <u>The show was enjoyed by everybody.</u>

b   A fire destroyed the factory.

→ _____

c   A whistle silenced the crowd.

→ _____

d   The sudden noise woke Sofia.

→ _____

e   The monster ate the car.

→ _____

2   Continue these passive sentences to reveal **who was responsible**.

a   The plate was broken by _____ .

b   The bag of gold was stolen _____ .

c   The man was hurt _____ .

d   The car was damaged _____ .

e   The lion was captured _____ .

Active and passive sentences 2

Explanation

In a **passive sentence** you can **hide the 'doer'** of the action. This can be useful when you don't want the reader to know who it is or when it is not important.

Example I **connected** the wires to the battery. ◄—— active
The wires **were connected** to the battery. ◄—— passive

Who did it is **not important** – the passive version is **less personal**, **more formal**.

Activities

1 Rewrite the following **active** sentences in the **passive** form and **hide the doer** of the actions. The first one has been done for you.

a ~~People~~ used pigeons to send messages.   Pigeons were used to send messages.

b ~~Someone~~ told the head teacher.   _____

c ~~We~~ sent the letter to the Prime Minister.   _____

d ~~Jim~~ stole the pirates' treasure.   _____

e ~~I~~ asked the people for their opinions.   _____

f ~~The wind~~ blew the oak tree over.   _____

2 In these sentences too, the **person** doing the action is **not important**. Rewrite the sentences in the passive form.

a We watered the plants every day.   The plants were watered every day.

b William invited the Mayor to the show.   _____

c The paramedics rushed Rory to hospital.   _____

d Fatima added salt to the water.   _____

e The class discussed a lot of ideas.   _____

Direct and reported speech

Explanation

There are two ways of writing down what someone says: you can use **direct speech** or **reported speech**.

Direct speech is when you write down exactly what is said using **speech marks** to show the spoken words.

Example 'I have no-one to help me,' said Mrs Anderson.

Reported speech is when you report what is said in your own words.

Example Mrs Anderson said that she had no-one to help her.

Activities

1 Here are some examples of **reported speech**. Write the character's words as **direct speech**.

a Louise said she hoped she could win the gold medal.

_____.

b Mr Hallam asked Rowan where he was going.

_____?

c Beth said that she would visit me later.

_____.

2 Change these examples of **direct** speech into **reported** speech.

a 'I know the answer!' announced Tara suddenly.

_____

b 'Does this path go through the forest?' asked Michael.

_____

c 'I found the key buried in the garden,' explained George.

_____

d 'It's all my fault,' said Rebecca.

_____

Grammar

Informal speech

When you speak to a friend, you probably use **informal speech**. You might use informal words and phrases and **shortened forms**. You probably use short or **incomplete sentences** and **exclamations**, or you **leave out words**.

Example Hey, did you see that?   What a mess!

Terrible, isn't it?   Should complain really.   Well, I mean …

question tag   'We' missed out   **ellipsis** (incomplete)

Activities

1 Read what these people say about their disastrous holidays. Choose **three** letters from the box and write them in the **squares** to label the features of **informal speech** used by each person.

A **shortened forms** (I'm, you're, it's)	B **question tags** (It is, isn't it?)	C **ellipsis** incomplete idea (missing words)	D **exclamations** (What a mess!)	E **speaks to the audience** (Did you hear?)

Mr Paul

Should've seen the pool. Filthy!

☐ ☐ ☐

Miss Elton

I'll get my money back, won't I? Hope so.

☐ ☐ ☐

Mr Patel

The room … you wouldn't believe it … really awful.

☐ ☐ ☐

Dr Archer

I tell you the hotel was terrible. The food … and the service … well!

☐ ☐ ☐

Sometimes you might use features of informal speech when writing a story or play. In a dialogue between two characters, informal speech can show that they are close friends, or that they are in a more relaxed setting.

Formal speech and writing

Explanation

In **formal situations** you should use **formal language**. In **formal speech** and **writing** simple things are said in a **longer**, more wordy style, using formal, **polite** language.

Example 'Hey, pass the salt, Freddie!' ⟵ at home
'Please may I have the salt, Frederick.' ⟵ at a formal
'Could you pass the salt, if it is not too much trouble.' ⟵ banquet

Formal writing uses longer sentences written in **Standard English** (see page 29), with no features of informal speech, shortened forms or missing words.

Activities

1 Draw a line to match each **informal phrase** with its **formal** alternative.

I reckon	please refrain from
if we all	suffice it to say
can you	it is my opinion that
don't	if everyone were to
enough said	if it were possible
sorry to say	I would be grateful if you could
if we could	I regret to inform you that

In **very formal writing**, look out for the **subjunctive** form of verbs after phrases such as 'I recommend/suggest/insist that …' or 'It is vital/essential that …'

Example I **propose that** Ava Bell **stand** for election.   (not: I **hope** Ava **stands**.)
I **propose that** Ava Bell **be** appointed pupil governor.   (not: I **hope** Ava **is** appointed.)

2 Here are some lines from a draft of a formal school letter. **Edit** each sentence, using features of **formal writing**.

a The school wants all pupils here on time.

b We'd like you to tell the teacher if your child's off sick.

c We'd like you to tell us about any doctor's appointments.

d To find out more, take a look at the school attendance policy on the website.

Formal writing

Formal writing is often **impersonal**.
Personal speech and writing speaks directly to the audience and uses personal pronouns such as **I**, **me**, **we**, **you**. **Impersonal** writing avoids using names or personal pronouns by using the passive voice or the impersonal pronoun **it**.

Example I think **you** should arrive early.   ◄——— personal
            It may be wise **to arrive** early.   ◄——— impersonal
            An early arrival would be advisable.   ◄——— impersonal

Activities

1 These sentences are written in a **personal** style. Write an **impersonal** version of each.

   a We don't have enough money left.

   _____

   b We have arranged a visit to the hospital.

   _____

   c I think it would be a good idea to wait until Monday.

   _____

   d Mr Hopkins expects us to be silent in assembly.

   _____

2 Rewrite each of these sentences as **formal**, **impersonal statements** that sound like **facts**.

   a My mum can't afford to buy the school uniform.

   _____

   b It takes me a long time to search the internet.

   _____

   c You can get a form from the Post Office.

   _____

   d My dog Oscar likes to run around.

   _____

Not all **formal speech** and **writing** is impersonal. A speech or a letter of complaint might be **personal** but still require formal language.

Letter to a friend

Write a letter to a friend or relative you have not seen for some time. Write news about yourself, your friends and family or local events. Include some things that have happened (using the past tense), what's happening right now (using the present tense) and future plans.

Single sentence postcards

Send a postcard with a message just one sentence long. See how much detail you can get into your single sentence. Start with a short sentence and expand noun phrases, and add adverbials and extra clauses to give more detail about who, what, where, why, when and how.

What if ...

This is a good way of exercising your imagination. Start with a blank piece of paper. Try to think of a really unusual situation – for example, if you shrank in the rain. Then think of all the things that might happen if this actually took place. Write your ideas as conditional sentences and fill the piece of paper with details of the amazing possibilities.

Scrapbook challenge

Make a scrapbook with photographs, cuttings, leaflets and pictures to remind yourself of events special to you. Write captions to explain each item. Challenge yourself to use different types of sentence: one-clause sentences, two-clause sentences, exclamations, a passive and so on.

Language collector

Collect examples of formal writing from leaflets, letters or newspapers. Listen for examples of formal speech on the television or at school – for example, listen to newsreaders, politicians, your head teacher. Copy or imitate these examples when you need to say things in a formal way.

Pass the story on

This is a fun way to write a story. Write the opening paragraph and add a linking adverbial to start the next paragraph. Pass the story to a friend to write the next paragraph and add the next adverbial. Choose intriguing adverbials such as 'at that moment'… 'nearby'… 'consequently', and see how the story develops.

Answers

Page 4: Nouns 1

1 These are just examples of sentences you might make. You may have used different nouns.

a The **elephant** sat on the **wall**.

b A **cow** jumped over the **moon**.

c My **mum** threw the **stick** into the **river**.

d The **man** was waiting for a **bus**.

e Asleep on the **grass** there was a great big **snake**.

2 These are just examples. You may have chosen different names.

a **Cuddles** the cat

b **Bubbles** the goldfish

c **Ozzie** the hamster

d **Mr Shaw** the teacher

e **Boris** the dog

f **Sid** the snake

g **Arnie** the lizard

h **Bunn's** the baker's

Page 5: Nouns 2

1 Here are some examples of noun phrases you might have included on your list.

Cake	Dog	Building
one chocolate éclair	our Yorkshire terrier	the Lo-Cost supermarket
this **Danish pastry**	a **Dalmatian puppy**	that **savings bank**
my **jam doughnut**	an **Alsatian**	two **primary schools**
an **Eccles cake**	that **poodle**	the **Science Museum**
six **fairy cakes**	her **pit bull terrier**	this **children's hospital**

2 These are just examples. You might have used different noun phrases.

a That **baby gorilla** stole my banana.

b **My little brother** ran into **Bragg's the baker's**.

c **Princess Ruby** stood in the middle of the **palace ballroom**.

d **Sergeant Major Smith** put on **his regiment's uniform**.

e **Three thieves** ran out of **New Street post office**.

Page 6: Adjectives 1

1 The **winding** path led her as far as the **crumbling** walls of an **abandoned** building. The **remaining** walls were **jagged** and **overgrown** with ivy. The ground was littered with **fallen** rubble.

2 These are just suggestions; there are many other adjectives that could be used.

a The **angry** alligators snapped at the **chattering** monkeys.

b The **foolish** cat sat on a **sleepy** hedgehog.

c The lion was **ferocious** but the mouse was **brave**.

d A **hungry** wolf waited in the **dark** wood.

e The **lonely** boy looked up at the **distant** moon.

f The **friendly** alien thought the planet looked **beautiful**.

g The man was **fearful** at the thought of crossing the **swollen** river.

h Rosie was **exhausted** after the **thrilling** game.

Page 7: Adjectives 2

1 Here are some suggestions for phrases you might have included. There are many possibilites.

Size	Colour	Qualities
enormous ears	a golden beak	a shy creature
a **long** tail	**bright** eyes	a **vicious** hunter
huge wings	**colourful** plumage	a **monstrous** beast
a **massive** body	**purple** patches	a **friendly** nature
tiny eyes	**dull brown** fur	a **fast** runner

2 This is just an example of adjectives that you might have used.

The sky was **heavy** and **grey**. It was **cold** and a few **feathery** flakes of snow were beginning to fall. Suddenly out of the gloom a **hunched** figure appeared hurrying down the road. The figure was **bent** and **sinister-looking**. It was wearing a **dark**, **flowing** cloak.

3 These are just examples of adjectives you might have used.

   a The **enchanted** forest was **quiet** and **still**.

   b The **little wooden** house was **warm** and **comforting**.

   c The **bleak** castle walls were **dark** and **forbidding**.

Page 8: Comparatives and superlatives

1 **a** clever → cleverer → cleverest

   b strong → **stronger** → **strongest**

   c fast → **faster** → **fastest**

   d good → better → **best**

2 These are just suggestions for how you might have completed the sentences.

   a My dad is cleverer than the winner of Mastermind.

   b Our dog is **louder** than **six car alarms**.

   c My sister is **funnier** than a **stand-up comedian**.

   d Our car is **faster** than **a speeding rocket**.

3 **a** Wheaty Flakes – the **crunchiest** cereal yet.

   b Don't miss the **funniest** film of the year.

   c Test-drive the **fastest** car on the track.

   d This is the **creamiest** ice cream ever tasted.

Page 9: Singular and plural

1 I need to buy a large pizza, **loaves of bread**, **bottles of pop**, a carton of milk, **lime jellies**, a pack of **streamers**, **cookies**, **party hats** and a cake.

2 **a** a tooth   many **teeth**

   b this woman   those **women**

   c one **gentleman**   two gentlemen

   d one foot   a pair of **feet**

   e a lone **deer**   a herd of deer

   f a single mouse   several **mice**

   g a goose   some **geese**

   h one **person**   various people

3 These are just examples. You may have chosen other singular and plural nouns.

   a The farmer has a **flock** of **sheep** and a number of **chickens**.

   b At the market I bought a few **computer games** and a **T-shirt**.

   c Waiting at the traffic lights, I saw several **cars** but only one **bus**.

   d On the beach I found countless **shells** but just one **crab**.

Page 10: Verbs 1

1 **a** The jet engines **roar** as the aeroplane **soars** into the sky.

   b From behind a tree, the cat **pounced** suddenly.

   c Carly **listened** for a moment before she **stepped** forward and **spoke**.

   d Tigers often **sleep** by day and **hunt** at night.

2 **a** Mr Samuels **has** a frightening temper.

   b Zebras **have** stripes.

   c Paris **is** the capital city of France.

   d Sophie and Isabelle **are** twins.

   e I **am** very happy today.

3 There are other possible sentences that could be made.

   a The **rain fell**.

   b A **building shook**.

   c The **king laughed**.

   d **Marcie groaned**.

Page 11: Verbs 2

1 These are just examples of powerful verbs that you could have used. There are lots of other possibilities.

   a The princess **glared** at the fisherman.

   b The giant **stomped** across the hillside.

   c The monster **gobbled** his food.

   d The girl **battled** through the trees.

   e 'It's not fair,' **moaned** Robbie.

   f The man **clambered** into the car.

2 These are just suggestions. Other verbs could be used.

Prince Fortune **strode** into the hall. He **glanced** across the room to where the queen and princess were **whispering** together.

3 **a** I **hear** a noise.   **c** I **race** outside.

   b It **is** late.   **d** He **falls** over.

Page 12: Adverbs 1

1 **a** slow**ly** **c** anxious**ly** **e** sweet**ly** **g** peaceful**ly** **i** quiet**ly** **k** polite**ly**
   b loud**ly** **d** bright**ly** **f** careful**ly** **h** sad**ly** **j** cheerful**ly** **l** excited**ly**

2 These are just examples of adverbs that you could have used. You might have chosen others.

 a The baby slept **peacefully** as we **quietly** left the room.

 b The crowd waited **excitedly** as the music played **loudly**.

 c She **slowly** opened the letter, **carefully** unfolding each page.

 d The audience listened **politely** as the choir sang **sweetly**.

 e He walked home **sadly** and **anxiously** waited for news.

 f The sun shone **brightly** as they **cheerfully** packed their bags.

Page 13: Adverbs 2

1 These are just examples. You may have chosen different adverbs or put them in different positions.

 a **Occasionally**, the man spoke to his neighbours.

 b They **soon** realised their mistake.

 c He walked **carefully** along the plank.

 d He hid the letters **upstairs**.

2 These are just suggestions. You may have chosen other adverbs that make sense.

 a **Fortunately**, everyone was safe.

 b **Obviously**, this was a serious mistake.

 c **Apparently**, the pool will close next month.

 d **Unfortunately**, the painting was destroyed.

Page 14: Prepositions 1

1 These are just suggestions. Other prepositional phrases could be used.

 a The boy climbed over the fence.

 b The girl jumped **into the hole**.

 c The man was standing **by the oak tree**.

 d The car drove **through the city**.

 e The ghost appeared **on the balcony**.

 f Marcus fell **in the swimming pool**.

2 These are just suggestions. Other prepositional phrases could be used.

 a **Before breakfast,** Jess went for a run.

 b **At midnight**, it began to rain.

 c **During the night**, all was quiet.

 d **After tea**, they couldn't go out.

 e **On Saturday**, we went to the cinema.

Page 15: Prepositions 2

1 These are just suggestions. Other prepositional phrases could be used.

 a The **cat with one ear** was sitting **by the gate**.

 b The **path through the wood** stopped **at the river**.

 c The **boy from outer space** travelled **in his spaceship**.

 d The **man in the red suit** was arrested **on Friday**.

 e The **book on the shelf** vanished **in the night**.

2 **a** Mix the flour and sugar together **in** a large bowl.

b Heat the butter and milk **over** a low heat.

c Roll out the mixture **with** a rolling pin.

d Place the biscuits **on** a baking tray.

e Take the biscuits out of the oven **after** 20 minutes.

f Leave them to cool **for** an hour.

Page 16: Pronouns 1

1 **a** **We** went to the shop but **it** was closed.

b Elliot had lost **his** coat and could not find **it** anywhere.

c The twins were playing in the garden but **their** sister did not see **them**.

d Nina knew that the book was **hers** but **she** did not want **it**.

e The man was following **us** and **we** were worried.

f Jordan thought **he** had won the race, but **he** should have looked behind **him**.

Page 17: Pronouns 2

1 The tortoise and the hare waited for the gun to start the race.
Bang! Immediately **the hare** flew out of the blocks. His long legs
ate up the ground and soon he was completely out of sight.
Meanwhile **the tortoise** had only just crossed the starting line. His little
legs did not move very fast. Looking back from the top of the hill **the hare** saw
the tortoise and laughed.

2 **a** It = the box   **b** that = **Will going first**   **c** This = **Hannah winning the race**   **d** It = **the film**

Page 18: Conjunctions

1 Some other conjunctions would also make sense in these sentences.

a The old man continued on his way **although** it was getting dark.

b Do not enter the room **unless** a green light is showing.

c Everyone rushed towards the river **as** the fire spread out of control.

d He fell asleep in his chair **because** he was so tired.

e **When** he saw the food, he gobbled it up immediately.

f **Since** it is already six o'clock, let's tidy away.

2 There are many possible endings for these sentences – these are just suggestions.

a The monster roared loudly when **he was disturbed**.

b The monster roared loudly because **someone had stepped on his tail**.

c The monster roared loudly although **there was no-one to hear him**.

d The monster roared loudly until **he realised no-one was listening**.

e The monster roared loudly so **we all ran away and hid**.

f The monster roared loudly while **the children screamed**.

Page 19: Editing: word choice

1 This is just an example. You may have used different words and phrases.

Two **opulent golden** doors opened to reveal the **magnificent** ballroom **with its five sparkling glass chandeliers**. The **long** room was full of **elegantly dressed** people, all dancing **in swirling patterns**. The walls were all **glistening** white and the **ornate** ceiling was patterned **with mosaics and intricate designs**. There were **rich** red **velvet** curtains hanging at the **tall bay** windows.

2 This is just an example of powerful verbs that could be used.

Grey-black clouds **rolled** across the sky. The branches on the trees **trembled** in the wind and the leaves **scattered** all around. Raindrops **splattered** on the windowpane and **exploded** in puddles on the pavement. People **scurried** down the road towards their homes. They **battled** with their umbrellas in the wind and rain.

Page 20: Understanding word classes 1

1 The thirsty elephant lumbered down to the watering hole.

    B   A   C   E

2 **a** noun adjective **b** verb **c** preposition **d** adverb **e** preposition

3 These are just examples. You may have thought of different sentences.

	Adjective	Noun	Verb	Prepositional phrase
The	chattering	monkey	swings	through the trees.
An	enormous	dog	bounded	down the hill.
The	annoying	wasp	landed	in the jam pot.
A	small	child	stood	by the playground gate.
A	red	car	careered	across the road.

Page 21: Understanding word classes 2

1 Tom hid **in the** shed **because he** was scared.

    B D   A   C

2 by

3 **The** doctor said that eating **an** apple **a** day is **a** good idea.

4 **a** We had lost **our** way. We shouted but no-one heard **us**.

    b They all went back to **their** rooms and left **me** by myself.

5 **a** before **b** until **c** after **d** as **e** but

6 This is just an example answer.

Three butterflies danced together in the ~~bright~~, dazzling, ~~glorious~~, early morning sunshine.

Page 22: Cohesion: linking ideas 1

1 **a** The children were hoping to go to the beach. **However**, it rained all day.

    b It was snowing heavily this morning. **As a result,** lots of people were late for school.

    c We visited the famous landmarks in Paris. **For example**, we went to the Eiffel Tower.

    d Our train was over an hour late. **Eventually**, we arrived at our destination.

    e Firstly, the trainers were not really what I wanted. **Secondly**, they were too expensive.

    f It was fine all day today. **In contrast**, it rained all yesterday.

2 These are just suggestions. The sentences could be completed in other ways.
  a Many people use their cars every day. For example, **they use them to travel to work**.
  b Many people use their cars every day. On the other hand, **some people prefer to use public transport**.
  c Many people use their cars every day. As a consequence, **there are too many cars on the roads**.
  d Many people use their cars every day. After all, **cars provide an easy way of getting around**.

Page 23: Cohesion: linking ideas 2

1 These are just suggestions. Other time connectives could be used.
Red Riding Hood was walking through the forest.
Suddenly, a wolf jumped out and surprised her.
After that, Red Riding Hood went on her way again.
Meanwhile, the wolf rushed to Granny's house.
Later, Red Riding Hood arrived at Granny's house.
Now, the wolf tried to eat Red Riding Hood.
At that moment, a woodcutter rushed in and killed the wolf.
Finally, everyone was safe.

2 These are just suggestions. The sentences could be completed in other ways.
  a It has not rained for several weeks. Consequently, the ground is very dry.
  b The wind fills the sails of the yacht. As a result, **the yacht moves forward**.
  c The handles on the bag were not very strong. Therefore, **they broke as soon as something heavy was put in it**.
  d The lions had not eaten for some time. Because of this **they were very dangerous**.

Page 24: Verb tenses 1

1 **a** It was hot last week.
  b I **heard** a strange sound.
  c I **jumped** high.
  d I **took** my time.
  e Ed **ran** for the bus.

2 You may have chosen different verbs but check that you have used the correct tense.
  a Birds live in trees where they **build** nests.
  b Cara realised she was late when she **missed** the bus.
  c I always help to wash up and **tidy** the kitchen.
  d We ate our breakfast before we **packed** our bags.
  e George enters and **sits** in the armchair.
  f He was tired as he **fell** into bed.

Page 25: Verb tenses 2

1 Marshall is leading at the bell but Jackson **is closing** on him again. The fans **are going** mad. Marshall **is sprinting** down the back straight but Jackson and the others **are chasing** hard.

2 Marshall was leading at the bell but Jackson **was closing** on him again. The fans **were going** mad. Marshall **was sprinting** down the back straight but Jackson and the others **were chasing** hard.

3 These are just examples. You may have chosen some different main verbs.

    a I **have seen** the film six times. It's great!

    b Mum says she **has written** a letter to the Prime Minister.

    c I think Dad **has gone/been** shopping.

    d I **have eaten** too much chocolate. Now I feel sick.

    e Be careful – someone **has broken** a glass.

    f You can't swim today if you **have forgotten** your trunks.

Page 26: First, second and third person 1

1 **a** My name is Megan and **I** live in Cardiff with **my** family.

    b The children tried to carry **their** bags but **they** were too heavy for **them**.

    c Have you ever had problems with **your** computer?

    d Mrs Quinn called Arthur and me into **her** office. **I** wondered what **we** had done.

    e He could not do it by **himself**. **He** needed someone to help **him**.

2 Lucy is 11 years old and she goes to Midfield School in Stonington. When she grows up she would really like to be a singer and have lots of hits.

Page 27: First, second and third person 2

1 I **had been working all day**, but still I had not caught one fish. I pulled up the last of my nets – it was empty, like all the others. I thought how unlucky I was. What would I tell my children? Just then something in the water caught my eye. I looked over the side of the boat to get a better look …

Page 28: Subject and verb agreement

1 **a** **He play** for the school team. ✗   **d** **They was** surprised by the result. ✗

    b **We were** really pleased. ✓   **e** Yes, **I done** it. ✗

    c **I hates** cheese and onion crisps. ✗   **f** **You have** five more minutes. ✓

2 He **plays** for the school team.   They **were** surprised by the result.

    Yes, I **did** it.   I **hate** cheese and onion crisps.

3 **a** You **are** happy.

    b She **has** lots of friends.

    c I **am** pleased.

    d They **have** a beautiful house.

    e He **is** tired.

Page 29: Standard English

1 **a** Zac and **me** ran all the way home.   I

    b Look at **them** horses in the field.   those

    c I **done** my homework last night.   did

    d I'll have one of **them** cakes.   those

    e This is the book **what** I read.   that

    f Here is a **real** funny joke.   really

2 **a** I never said anything.

  b Nobody did **anything** to help.

  c I saw nobody.

  d I don't like **anything** here.

Page 30: Editing: checking consistency

1 On Saturday, we went **to** watch the school football team play in the
Player's Cup. It **was** a very exciting game. The final score was 2–2, **which** was
probably a fair result because both teams **played** well. Our team **scored**
first thanks to **an** awesome free kick from Jake Edwards. But
then they **equalised** just before the whistle **went** for half-time.

2 **a** Evie and Emily had left **their** coats on the bus.

  b Jack ran to the top of the beanstalk and **the giant** ran after him.

  c After we finished, Jordan and **I** were exhausted.

  d Becky was worried about Ethan and me. She tried to call **us**.

  e David couldn't open the door without the wizard's key. **The door** was locked and **David**
knew **the key** was still in **the wizard's** workshop.

Page 31: Editing: grammatical errors

1 **a** The old man said he **weren't** hungry.   wasn't

  b I think the computer is **broked**.   broken

  c Everyone **have** forgotten about us.   has

  d Mrs Gardiner **gived** me **them** old photos.   gave, those

  e The film **what** I saw was **real** sad.   that, really

  f I have **writ** the date in **me** diary.   written, my

2 Let me tell you about my family. We live in a house on the corner of Grant Street.
I **have** two sisters and **an** older brother. My sisters **are** twins. My brother and
I share a room. My brother says he **doesn't** like sharing with me because he
hasn't **any** (or **has no**) space for his things. Sometimes the twins and I play together,
but sometimes we argue.

Page 32: Phrases and clauses

1 **a** clause   **b** phrase   **c** phrase   **d** clause   **e** clause   **f** phrase

2 These are just suggestions. There are many ways to complete the sentences.

  a **In the morning** the teacher was furious **with the class**.

  b **Within seconds** the robber had escaped **in a car**.

  c **Only the other day** a boy slipped **in the corridor**.

  d **In the morning** I saw Mrs Johnson **in the corridor**.

Page 33: One-clause sentences

1 These are just suggestions. There are many ways to complete the sentences.

   a The angry lion glared through the metal bars.

   b **The vase shattered into** pieces on the floor.

   c **The rabbit had a pink**, **twitchy nose and** two pointed ears.

   d **It rained** on the way to school.

   e The excited children **screeched loudly**.

2 This is just a suggestion. There are many sentences you could make.

   <u>The old lady</u> chased the mouse around the kitchen.

3 You may have ended your sentences differently.

   a The horse trotted down the road.

   b The rock climbers **clambered to the top of the cliff**.

   c The witch **vanished in a puff of smoke**.

   d A butterfly **fluttered past the window**.

   e A dog **barked outside**.

Page 34: Joining main clauses

1 **a** I missed the bus **but** I wasn't late.

   b The windows were open **and** I could hear birds singing.

   c He picked up all the rubbish **and** he put it in the bin.

   d It will be dry in the north **but** there will be rain in the south.

   e We could go to the zoo **or** we could go into town.

2 These are just suggestions; the sentences could be finished in many ways.

   a The car stopped and **two policemen jumped out**.

      The car stopped but **no-one got out**.

   b Alex was tired but **he still had a lot to do**.

      Alex was tired and **he needed a rest**.

   c Simone can play football but **she is not in the school team**.

      Simone can play football or **she can watch TV**.

Page 35: Subordinate clauses 1

1 **a** <u>The dog snarled at her</u>, which made her nervous.

   b Although his heart was pounding, <u>Emil stepped forward</u>.

   c While she was reading, <u>the doorbell rang</u>.

   d <u>The lights came on one at a time</u> until the whole street was lit up.

   e When the factory closed, <u>many people lost their jobs</u>.

   f <u>Stretch the fabric over the card</u>, folding the edges under neatly.

2 These are just suggestions.

a As it was dark, **we needed a torch**.

b When we arrived home, **I went straight to bed**.

c **We huddled by the fire** because it was cold.

d **Mrs Mills bought a new car** after winning the lottery.

e **Everyone laughed at the clown** when he fell over.

f Peering through the window, **I could see the two men**.

g **James was late again**, which really annoyed me.

Page 36: Subordinate clauses 2

1 These are just suggestions for subordinate clause to fit the conjunctions.

a Dad enjoys cooking because **he finds it relaxing**.

b Dad enjoys cooking whenever **he has the time**.

c Dad enjoys cooking whereas **Mum hates it**.

d Dad enjoys cooking until **he has to wash up**.

e Dad enjoys cooking though **he likes eating more**.

f Dad enjoys cooking as long as **no-one disturbs him**.

2 a **Standing by the door**, Ellen watched the storm approaching.

b **Travelling at speed**, the car just missed the approaching lorry.

c **Encouraged by the crowd**, the runner sprinted for the line.

Page 37: Relative clauses

1 a Paula, **who was exhausted**, refused to move.

b Mr King, **who had left early**, was now very late.

c The beggar, **who was penniless**, pleaded for help.

d The house, **which is now empty**, once belonged to my father.

e The vase, **which was broken**, lay on the floor.

2 a We found the street **where** Tarik lives.

b Today was the exam **that** she was dreading.

c I saw Joanna, **whose** mother was waiting outside.

d That was the day **when** it all began.

e He chose the red door, **which** was a mistake.

Page 38: Sentence types 1

1 a **Statement** You are planning a holiday.   **Question** Are you planning a holiday?

b **Statement** It is cold.   **Question** Is it cold?

c **Statement** You are bored.   **Question** Are you bored?

d **Statement** You can help me.   **Question** Can you help me?

2 a Take the dog for a walk every day.   c Eat lots of fruit and vegetables.

b Visit Hammington Hall this weekend.

Page 39: Sentence types 2

1 a This game is really simple. ☑   There should be five counters. ☑
       Take out the pieces. ☐   Are you ready to play? ☐
       Place them on the table. ☐   Let's go. ☐

   b Take (out), Place, Let's   c Let's go!

2 a Help me.   c Put that down.   e Come and visit soon.
   b Hold this end.   d Try this new ice cream.

3 a question   b command   c statement

Page 40: Placing adverbials

1 These are just some possibilities – you may have chosen a different version of the sentences.
   a **Hurriedly**, the princess dropped the message **out of the window**.
   b **At midnight**, the villagers were waiting **anxiously**.
   c **During this time**, the explorers **frequently** went without food.
   d **At school**, Danny was **usually** in trouble.

2 He strode purposefully through the town.
   Purposefully, he strode through the town.
   Through the town he strode purposefully.

Page 41: Placing subordinate clauses

1 a **Until the storm began**, everything was quiet.
   b **Humming merrily**, the man strolled along the street.
   c **Despite playing extra time**, the match was a draw.
   d **To achieve perfection**, she had to train hard.

2 These are just suggestions. The sentences could be completed in many ways.
   a **Cheated of his fortune**, the man returned home.
   b **While the wolf wasn't looking**, Tim hid in the tree.
   c **Although she was exhausted**, she did not stop.
   d **Once the robbers had piled in**, the car sped off.
   e **While the poor serving girl sobbed**, the evil queen laughed.

3 I won't know **until I receive the letter** if I have won.

Page 42: Multi-clause sentences

1 These are just suggestions. There are other ways of combining the sentences.
   a **As** the sun began to rise, the grey world became lighter **and** the birds awoke from their sleep.
   b **Feeling** more confident, **Lee** climbed to the top of the ladder, **where** he paused for a moment.
   c The sloth, **a** slow-moving mammal, lives in trees **where** it hangs upside down from branches.
   d **Walking** quickly, he followed the mysterious figure **as** it crossed the marketplace.
   e **As** the waves wash over the cliffs, some rocks are worn away **and** fall into the sea.

Page 43: Editing: sentence construction

1 This is just an example. You may have formed different sentences.
One day Anya and Leon went to the canal **to go** fishing. There seemed to be no-one else around **so** they chose the best place **and** started to get out the rods. Suddenly there was a loud splash **followed by** a scream. **As** Anya and Leon looked up they saw something moving in the water. **There was** a hand waving. Someone had fallen **in**.

2 This is just one way of splitting the text into separate sentences. You may have found a different way.
Human beings need food in order to live. **Every** part of the body needs a steady supply of food so that it can work properly. **First** the food has to be broken down through a process called digestion. **This allows the food** to dissolve in the blood and travel around the body.

3 These are just examples of the sentences you may have written.
Question Are you bored by slow, dull computer games?
Statement Manic Heroes is a fantastic new computer game for kids.
Command Order it today.
Exclamation It's great!

Page 44: Understanding sentence terms

1 Mr Watkins lost his umbrella.

2 You may not have written exactly this sentence.
The little dog barked at the big dog.

3 These are just examples of the sentences you may have written.
  a Mr Watkins did not lose his umbrella.
  b The big dog never barks at the little dog.

4 These are just examples of the sentences you may have written.
  a Mr Watkins lost his umbrella, **but luckily it did not rain**.
  b Mr Watkins, **who is rather forgetful**, lost his umbrella.
  c **As the wind blew**, Mr Watkins lost his umbrella.

5 **a** I'd like to help Mr Watkins but I cannot (help Mr Watkins).
  b Mr Watkins found his umbrella and (Mr Watkins) put it up.
  c I gave him my umbrella because I wanted to (give him my umbrella).

Page 46: Possibility: modal verbs

You may have used a different modal verb in some of these sentences.

1 **a** We **could** win our next game.
  b It **might** rain tomorrow.
  c She **may** be late today.
  d I **might** see you tomorrow.
  e I **may** go out later.
  f It **could** work.

2 **a** It **will** help.
  b You **shall** go to the ball.
  c It **must** be true.
  d We **can** do this.
  e I **shall** be there.
  f It **will** be cold.

3 a I **may** have the answer.

b She **could** win first prize.

c This **might** solve the problem.

d It **may** be his best book yet.

e It **might** be too late.

4 This is just an example of what you might have written.

In the week ahead you could meet lots of new and interesting people. You **will** learn lots of new things. There **may** be many exciting opportunities. You **might** have some problems to overcome but you **will** succeed.

Page 47: Possibility: adverbs

1 **Very likely**: certainly, surely, definitely

Possible: possibly, maybe, perhaps

Not very likely: rarely, never, seldom

2 You may have used a different adverb in some of these sentences.

a He will **definitely** succeed.

b This is **clearly** the best.

c **Of course**, it will work.

d **Obviously** he told the truth

e This plant will **surely** die.

f I will **certainly** be there.

g They are **surely** wrong.

h It will **almost certainly** rain today.

3 These are just examples of how you could complete the sentences.

a The letter did not arrive today. Maybe **it will come tomorrow**.

b Our star striker is injured. He might possibly **be back next week**.

c I have lost my coat. Perhaps **I left it outside**.

d Max did not come. He probably **forgot about the meeting**.

e We can't do this alone. Maybe **Ella can help us**.

f It is still raining. Perhaps **the weather will improve tomorrow**.

Page 48: Conditional sentences 1

1 These are just suggestions for the sort of main clauses needed.

a If I had a magic wand, **I would turn someone into a frog**.

b If I were famous, **I would live in a huge mansion**.

c **I would take a long holiday** if I won the lottery.

d If I were invisible, **I would play tricks on my friends**.

e If I had a magic carpet, **I would fly round the world**.

f **I would ban fighting** if I ruled the world,

2 These are just suggestions for the sort of clauses needed.

a If we continue to destroy the forests, **many habitats will be lost**.

b If everyone drops litter in the street, **our town will look a mess**.

c If everyone switches off one light, **we will save electricity**.

d If Jack decides to climb the beanstalk, **he will meet a giant**.

e If they cannot escape from the dragon's cave, **they will be eaten**.

f **We will improve** if we all practise hard.

Page 49: Conditional sentences 2

1 These are just suggestions for how you might have completed the sentences.

a If it continues to rain, we will **need our umbrellas**.

If it continues to rain we could **be flooded**.

If it continues to rain we might **need a boat** or we may even **need to build an ark**.

b If I keep practising I will **get better**.

If I keep practising I could **represent my school**.

If I keep practising I might **represent my country one day** and I may even **win an Olympic medal**.

2 These are just suggestions for the sort of clauses needed.

a If you had picked up the banana skin, I would not have slipped over.

b If **we had scored that penalty**, we could have won the game.

c If **I had left earlier**, I might have arrived on time.

d If **you had revised**, you might have known the answer.

e If **the car had not swerved**, it would have hit the lorry.

f If **I had been up early**, I could have seen the sunrise.

Page 50: Active and passive sentences 1

1 **a** The show **was enjoyed** by everybody.

b The factory **was destroyed** by a fire.

c The crowd **was silenced** by a whistle.

d Sofia **was woken by** the sudden noise.

e The car **was eaten by** the monster.

2 These are just suggestions. You probably ended your sentences differently.

a The plate was broken by **my clumsy sister**.

b The bag of gold was stolen **by the wicked elves**.

c The man was hurt **by the lies**.

d The car was damaged **by the falling tree**.

e The lion was captured **by the brave zookeeper**.

Page 51: Active and passive sentences 2

1 **a** Pigeons were used to send messages.

b The head teacher **was told**.

c The letter **was sent** to the Prime Minister.

d The pirates' treasure **was stolen**.

e People **were asked** for their opinions.

f The oak tree **was blown** over.

2 **a** The plants were watered every day.

b The Mayor **was invited** to the show.

c Rory **was rushed** to hospital.

d Salt **was added** to the water.

e A lot of ideas **were discussed**.

Page 52: Direct and reported speech

1 a 'I hope I can win the gold medal,' said Louise.

  b 'Where are you going, Rowan?' asked Mr Hallam.

  c 'I will visit you later,' said Beth.

2 a Suddenly Tara announced **that she knew the answer**.

  b Michael asked **whether the path went through the forest**.

  c George explained **that he had found the key buried in the garden**.

  d Rebecca said **that it was all her fault**.

Page 53: Informal speech

1 Mr Paul **A C D**   Miss Elton **A B C**   Mr Patel **A C E**   Dr Archer **C D E**

Page 54: Formal speech and writing

1

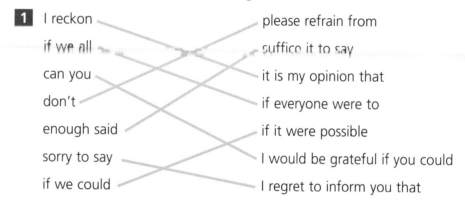

I reckon	please refrain from
if we all	suffice it to say
can you	it is my opinion that
don't	if everyone were to
enough said	if it were possible
sorry to say	I would be grateful if you could
if we could	I regret to inform you that

2 These are examples to show how a more formal tone could be achieved.

  a The school **requires that** all pupils **be punctual**.

  b **We ask that you inform** the teacher of any **absence due to illness**.

  c **It is essential that** the school **be kept fully informed** of any **medical appointments**.

  d **For more details, please refer to** the school's attendance policy, which **can be found** on the website.

Page 55: Formal writing

1 These are examples to show how a more formal tone could be achieved.

  a **There is** not enough money left. Or: **There are** insufficient funds available.

  b A visit to the hospital **has been arranged**.

  c **It may be wise** to wait until Monday.

  d Silence **is expected** in assembly.

2 a **School uniform can be** expensive.

  b **Searching the internet can be** time consuming.

  c **Forms can be obtained** from the post office.

  d **All dogs like** the freedom to run around.